If...
The Story of
Faith Walker

By
Florenza Denise Lee

If, The Story of Faith Walker
A Christian Young Reader Chapter Book highlighting the importance of faith, perseverance, acceptance, and the bonds of friendship and family.

Text and Illustrations copyright @ 2019 by Words to Ponder Publishing Company, LLC. Text design and cover art by Sofania.

First Printing

Address of inquiries to Contact@florenza.org

Hardcover Printed Version ISBN 978-1-941328-17-0
Softcover Printed Version ISBN 978-1-941328-11-8
eBook Version ISBN: 978-1-941328-16-3

Words to Ponder Publishing Company, LLC
Printed in the United States of America
For more information, visit https://www.florenza.org

Published titles by Florenza include:

Barry Bear's Very Best, Learning to Say No to Negative Influences

The Tail of Max the Mindless Dog, A Children's Book on Mindfulness

Welcome Home Daddy Love, Lexi

Children's Books coming soon are:

Acornsville, Land of the Secret Seed Keepers

Adventurous Olivia's Alphabet Quest

Amiri's Birthday Wish

Micah and Malik's Super Awesome Excellent Adventure

Oh, My Goodness, Look at this Big Mess

Two Bees in a Hive

When Life Gives Us Wind

Young Reader Chapter Books coming soon are:

Hoku to the Rescue

No Place Like My Own Home

Two-Thirds is a Whole

For more information regarding Florenza's books, or to contact her to speak at your school or event, please visit www.florenza.org.

Acknowledgment

Firstly, I want to publicly acknowledge the support of my spectacular family! Trefus, Jessica, Missy, and yes, even our fur-baby, Hoku, I could not do what I do without your love and assistance. Next, I acknowledge the hard work and dedication of those who behold my passion of writing and come alongside to lend their talents, gifts, encouragement, support, correction, energy, and "all other needs as required."

I say that I am a transcriber; God shows me the vision of my books, and in obedience, I transcribe what I sense and behold. But I could not create an actual book without your backing. Lastly, I want to thank my remarkable editors who ensure that my words are appropriately dressed for the eyes of my wonderful readers! I thank each one of you, from the bottom of my heart!

Foreword

As youth pastors, my wife Lauren and I understand how important it is for every child to recognize his or her God-given talents; doing so allows them to walk in purpose. Lauren and I have witnessed firsthand Florenza's passion for developing and encouraging children to hone their spiritual abilities and gifts. Through her powerfully written books, Florenza emboldens children to rise above conflict, bullying, insecurities, doubt, and fear.

In *If, The Story of Faith Walker,* Florenza takes us on a fabulous journey to witness Imani's faith as she rises above adversity in pursuit of her dream. We walk with Imani during discoveries of her passion and talent. She allows no obstacle to stand in her way; like Peter, she trusts in Jesus to walk on water. The fulfillment of Imani's dreams will enable her to overflow with joy and purpose. *If* is compelling and, at times, humorous. What it is not, is preaching or stuffy. *If* is sure to empower your children to trust God to fulfill all of His promises given to them.

Caleb Harris, Youth Pastor

Warwick Assembly Church

Hampton, VA

Dedication Page

I dedicate this book to all who walk by faith and not by sight.

Florenza

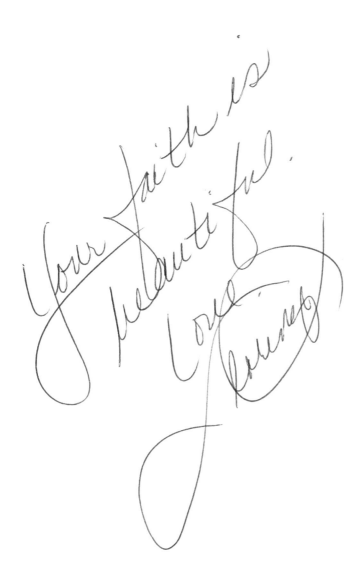

Life is full of happiness and tears; be strong and have faith.

∼ Kareena Kapoor Khan

Contents

Chapter One

What Did I Just Hear?

"**A**lright, everyone, time to listen up."

I am amazed at how teachers believe that after overloading kids with sugar and getting them rowdy from playing games, they can just magically flip the off switch by declaring, "listen up." It doesn't work like that, no matter the setting.

"Open your Bibles to the New Testament; our Scripture text is located in Matthew 14. Today, we will discuss the miracle Peter experienced with Christ. Sarah, please read verses 22 through 33." Pastor Caleb is our youth church leader, and he's just alright. Just kidding, he is actually very cool. He's been attending this church his entire life. He grew up here and is now the leader; crazy right?

"Geez, that's ten verses?" I mumble under my breath, "She will be reading the entire service." I know subconsciously you believe I should be paying attention, and you are probably right! After all, this is church. I agree, but I'll use this time to check out my social media sites. Nowadays, most kids in church use their phones as their Bibles anyway. With any luck, I can take a sneak peek without getting caught. Well, that's the plan.

While secretly swiping past pictures of food (man, people take a heck of a lot of pictures of their food!), and photos of girls with bunny ears and floating gold stars around their heads (I can never understand the appeal of silly filters), I overhear something that immediately catches my attention. Jerking my head up from my phone, I ask myself, "Wait! What did I just hear?"

"'If it's you,' Peter replied, 'tell me to come to you on the water,'" Sarah reads.

Quickly opening my online Bible app (I obviously should have been paying attention), I attempt to recall the verse Pastor Caleb gave; what was it? Now I got it! Matthew 14. Allowing a few seconds to actually locate it, I begin reading:

～

Immediately Jesus made the disciples get into the boat and go on ahead of him to the other side, while he dismissed the crowd. After he had dismissed them, he went up on a mountainside by himself to pray. Later that night, he was there alone, and the boat was already a considerable distance from land, buffeted by the waves because the wind was against it.

Shortly before dawn, Jesus went out to them, walking on the lake. When the disciples saw him walking on the lake, they were terrified. "It's a ghost," they said and cried out in fear.

But Jesus immediately said to them: "Take courage! It is I. Don't be afraid."

"Lord, if it's you," Peter replied, "tell me to come to you on the water."

"Come," he said.

Then Peter got down out of the boat, walked on the water and came toward Jesus. But when he saw the wind, he was afraid and, beginning to sink, cried out, "Lord, save me!"

Immediately Jesus reached out his hand and caught him. "You of little faith," he said, "why did you doubt?"

And when they climbed into the boat, the wind died down. Then those who were in the boat worshiped him, saying, "Truly you are the Son of God."

∿

Before anyone else asks a question, my arm goes straight up like a rocket. Not even waiting to be called upon, I yell, "Pastor Caleb, did this absolutely happen? I mean, did Peter ACTUALLY walk on water, literally?"

All heads turn my way. Some are gawking because, like me, they genuinely want to know the answer. Others are looking because they are stunned to hear my voice. Usually, I sit silently at the back of the class. I am an "observer" in youth church, not a "participant." I have my own issues and try particularly hard to fly under the radar.

Ha! Who the heck am I kidding! My very existence IS THE RADAR. When I enter into a room, all eyes are immediately on me, no matter what else is occurring! Without me even uttering a single word, my presence screams, "Hey, everyone! Turn your heads this way. Look right here!"

Pastor Caleb smiles and replies with the voice of complete conviction, "That is a great question, and to answer it, yes, Imani, it did happen. If it is recorded in the Bible, it happened precisely as it reads. You can take that to the bank."

He delays as if I have something else to ask. When nothing follows, he selects another hand that is raised. While others are asking their questions, I instantly return to my phone. No, I am not viewing social media pictures, I am genuinely rereading those verses. I bet you are as flabbergasted as I am. There is something in these words I perceive I need to concentrate on. I don't quite comprehend it, but something is drawing me into the verses. It's like I'm on a quest to discover a solution to a puzzle; a mystery I didn't even know needed to be solved.

As the class is moving on, I can't help it, I go back and read it again and again. I am so focused; I wouldn't be surprised if others assume that I'm surfing the net. At this point, they can believe whatever they want. I sense I am on an assignment.

"Your attention, please," announces Ms. Lauren, Pastor Caleb's wife. I sincerely adore her; she has a way of identifying the person inside of the person. Lauren looks beyond what others visualize on the outside and observes the heart. She also gives the best hugs ever! It is like being hugged by your favorite blanket or stuffed animal. She is caring, patient, and super affectionate.

"Service is coming to an end; it is almost time to go home. Be sure to retrieve your belongings before you head next door. Your folks will be coming up in approximately 15 minutes. Guys, make an effort to have a fantastic week and don't forget to carve out time in your schedule to pray, read your Bible, and most importantly, listen for God to speak to your hearts. He is continuously speaking; it is our responsibility to train our hearts to listen." Ms. Lauren walks around the room, hugging each of us as we head over to the game room.

The game room is dope! It has all sorts of things to do. Air hockey, board games, a reading nook with lots of marvelous books, and an area where you can work on devotions. It is also the hangout area where we get caught up with each other. Our church is kind of big, not quite a mega-church or anything like that, but significant, nonetheless. Kids come from different schools, neighborhoods, all over the place. Of course, we talk on the phone, but this is our time to quite frankly connect. It is more than church; it is our family time.

We enter the room. Kids are hype! They are chatting, playing games, and arguing over who just cheated on the video game; I locate a quiet area to reflect. I'm deep in reflection when my folks come to the door. Inevitably, Mom has her phone glued to her ear. She advocates for exploited and abused children and is frequently on call. I can't complain. Her love for children is the reason why I get to call her Mom.

"Hey, Shorty." You may not be able to tell, but that's my dad! "How was youth church?" he inquires as I accompany them in the hall. He is incredible and chilled; a great combination! He is the very opposite of my mom; she is frequently rolling a mile a minute, but nothing ruffles his feathers. He is easy-peasy. People say this is the reason why they make a great couple. I guess so. They need each other to balance themselves out, and I need both of them to balance me out. Combined, we make a great crew.

"Backatcha," I say. "We had a fantastic service. We discussed Peter walking on water and stuff."

"That is one of my all-time favorite Bible stories. It is so powerful. What was your takeaway?" he asks as we make our way to the vehicle. My mom is in front of us, yakking away. She perceives us talking and glances back at me as she silently says, "I am almost done. Love you, Mani."

"I think I have a few questions about it but give me a couple of days. I want to read it some more."

"Forever available to chat if you have questions, you know that."

"I do, Dad. Thanks." My father isn't a pastor or anything like that, but he honestly loves God and the Bible. He keeps open communication with me, to come to ask anything I want about it, and never judges me or causes me to feel like I should already know it. He explains things in a way that actually help it all make sense. I told you he is incredible.

We get in the car to go get lunch. Sundays are our family days. Traditionally, we go out someplace to eat. It allows us to enjoy some together time without having to clean the house afterward.

It gives us all a break. I love our family times, but it is not entirely easy for me. When we go to a new diner to eat, or when we are at one of our favorite spots, and new customers come in, it can be a bit uncomfortable. Folks tend to stare.

Oh, wait, where are my manners? I don't think you know. When I was born, I was just like all the other babies, a little chubby thing with ten toes and fingers and button nose. Nothing appeared to be different. Then I developed Meningitis B, and both my legs and arms (just past my knees and elbows) were amputated. While in the hospital, my womb-mom, who was single and very young, couldn't handle the stress, she went for a walk, and never came back. I was abandoned. Wonderfully sympathetic nurses cared for me until I was well enough to go into foster care.

Janet, one of the incredible nurses who took care of me (and who later became my godmother), told her best friend Maya how precious she felt I was, and well, Maya eventually became my mom. She and David adopted me when I was just a few months old. They have loved me like their very own each and every day. I have days when I would like to know more about my biological parents, but I would not change a single thing. I have a marvelous life. The way I look at it, my womb-mom birthed me, but Janet and Maya gave me life. I got a two-for-one mom deal!"

Sitting at dinner, listening to my parents talk about the sermon Pastor Jim preached, and me sharing the lesson Pastor Caleb spoke, makes me feel all warm and fuzzy inside. I whole-heartedly cherish my family. I can't envision having any other life but the one I have.

Chapter Two

Nothing Is Impossible

Later in the week, while in class, I still have the Bible verse in my head; I just can't seem to stop speculating; it has me discombobulated! Something is calling me from Peter's words, "If that is really you, then tell me to come." I must focus; Mrs. King is discussing the study notes for our upcoming test. She says there is absolutely no excuse to not do well in her class. She is known for caring over, above, and far beyond the norm to ensure her students have everything they need to excel. When we succeed, she succeeds. Those are her words, not mine.

"Class, please do due diligence and pay attention to the information on pages 10 - 25 in your book. You will have multiple choice and a few essay questions. I am looking for well-thought-out responses, not canned replies. You guys are magnificent writers, and I expect this to be reflected in your answers."

As the clock winds down and lunchtime approaches, Renee, my bestie, is already sending me the silent signal. It denotes she has some juicy gossip she wants to share during lunch. Renee definitely has the absolute best insider information and could emcee her own gossip channel talk show. She would be a stellar announcer. Renee is so darned animated when communicating. Her entire body moves as she speaks.

Renee and I met when she moved into our neighborhood. Her family bought the house directly next door to us. The previous neighbors were older, and they had no kids or grandkids. The way the homes are situated, they are slightly far apart; only a few are on the street. The other families have adult children who only visit occasionally. So, for a long time, it was just me. Having a family with kids my age move in next door was a huge score.

That day, as the movers were struggling in the heat to unload their furniture, she waltzed right over wearing cut off shorts and a brightly colored blouse with super full sleeves. Renee looked like she was floating on air when she walked up. Her bright red hair was bouncing as she strutted towards me. I could tell right then and there she was a diva.

"Hey, hey," she announces as soon as she was within earshot, "my name is Renee, but you can call me Renee," she then burst out laughing at her own joke.

As she made her way closer, I saw she had the most incredible green eyes; they literally looked like marbles; the kind kids used to play with when TV was black and white. She had enough freckles to replicate the Milky Way.

"Hey, my name is Imani. Are you guys moving in?"

"Yep, we moved from Ohio. My dad declared he has had enough

of the frigid cold weather, and we needed to head south. How long have you lived here?" she asked, seeming to not even notice we were not speaking eye to eye. That afternoon, I was outside without my prosthetics and was in my motorized wheelchair; she seemed to not even care. This is what made me like her the most.

I don't usually use my chair when I'm at my house, I just scoot around. I started scooting as soon as my parents brought me home. They wanted me to be as independent a kid as possible, so they allowed me to develop naturally. They let me try and try again before stepping in to assist me in whatever task I was doing. As I grew older, they would ask if I needed assistance before stepping in to help me, and if I replied, "No," they sat back and let me figure it out. This is the best gift they ever gave me outside of their unconditional love.

"I am known to sort of gossip a lot," she indicated, "so, any good, juicy intel you can give me is greatly appreciated."

"Well, I don't gossip, but absolutely, I will share what I can." With that, Renee sat down on the sidewalk, and we talked for hours as the movers unloaded their stuff. That was a few years back, and we have been best friends ever since.

The bell rings, and she walks beside me as I maneuver my chair through the halls toward the lunchroom. We get our food and head to our favorite spot. Since our school is in a rural community, we have outdoor and indoor eating spaces. Renee and I have a little area outside that allows us to talk without everyone eavesdropping. We discovered it her first day at Edwin Lee Intermediate School. The building houses grades K through eighth. The population is small, so everyone knows everyone. It's at times beneficial but can also be a pain. Everybody knows your business, and once Renee knows it, it might as well be on CNN! I told you she could have her own TV show.

"Girl, I have to tell you what I just heard," she states between bites. "The teen center is having a talent show. Mr. Burton, you know the guy who runs that organization, Our Youth Our Future Foundation, Inc.? Well, they are having a talent showcase in a month, and I think you should enter.

Whoa! That came out of left field! I assumed she was preparing to tell me something she heard through the grapevine about somebody getting caught cheating on a test or kissing in the halls. I was not ready to be asked to enter a contest.

"Renee? Did you fall and hit your head or something? You know I will not entertain the idea of performing in a talent show."

"Well, I think differently! I believe you should consider it. I know you have been practicing your rapping, and I saw those moves you have been secretly performing in your backyard. Girl, you are terrific. Why don't you complete an application?"

I tell her she is insane and needs to get her head examined. We finish our lunch just as the warning bell sounds, then make our way back to class. The entire rest of the day, I am contemplating the contest and her words in my ear. First, I never even knew she was watching me. She is my best friend, but even besties don't know everything about you. Some things need to be kept secret. I don't think my folks know I have been practicing dance moves.

Out of nowhere, I hear, "If it's you, tell me to come to you on the water." This is not the water I think Peter was talking about. I push it out of my mind and pay attention in class. No matter how much I focus, I keep replaying Renee's voice telling me I am terrific and continue reasoning about the Bible verses. "Get it together, girl," I whisper to myself.

After school, Renee comes over so we can study for our upcoming test. She and I have a running competition in class. We challenge each other to determine who will get the highest grades. This started right after we realized we were in the same classroom. Between the two of us, we are consistently the top scorers in the class. Rather than be jealous of one another, we started making it our personal competition. We've periodically had other students slam both of us and take the top seat. But that doesn't usually last long. We are equally fierce competitors, and it keeps us both on our study game.

"Did you hear Michael and Angie broke up?" she says.

"What? Again?"

"Yeah, they do it every other month."

"I think they should focus on themselves and stop with the foolishness," I say as I yawn, then close my book. I have had enough studying for one day. "You wanna go over to the park?"

"Sure, the weather is perfect for a stroll, let's walk over," she replies as she, too, closes her book.

"Hey, Dad," I yell as we are heading out the front door, "Renee and I taking a quick walk to the park. I have my phone with me. We won't be gone too long."

"Alright girls, have fun. Be safe, and don't stay too late. It's almost time for dinner."

Once we are outside, I ask, "Renee, how is your brother doing?"

"He is doing OK. He's having a rough time with some of the drill sergeants. He says it is harder than he initially believed but is ecstatic he enlisted. Josh says joining is the best decision he ever made for himself. He's already learning discipline and how to be a team player. The Army is all he talks about. You should hear him. It is like someone else is on the phone when he calls."

"Oh wow, I am so happy to hear that. I know being in a small town is not for everyone. I'm so glad your brother found his calling and got moving before he started getting into trouble. How is your dad doing with him being in the Army? Your dad was a Marine, right?"

"Ha, yeah, and don't ever let him catch you repeating that phrase, 'was a Marine.' Dad says, 'once a Marine, ALWAYS a Marine.' You should observe the two of them talking. It's funny; Dad is all, 'The few, the proud, the Marines.' And Josh is all, 'Hooah! Hooah! Army strong!' I notice the pride and respect in my dad's eyes when he is talking to Joshua. Dad is thrilled that Josh is doing something productive with his life. He should be home next month. I can't wait to hug him. Speaking of next month, have you considered any more about the talent show? I believe your performance is a perfect fit. Who knows, you may bring home the prize."

"Enough about that contest. Why don't YOU enter it? You are the one with all the talent. How many years have you been studying ballet? Like 50 or something?" She slaps me on the shoulder as I say that.

Renee has been performing since she was four years old, and she is quite superb! She started learning this new form of dance that has a hip-hop beat to it. Her folks were not too sure about it at first, but she actually loved it, and in time became so good, they started liking it also. It took them a long time to get adjusted to hearing the music, though. They are straight country folk and used to say the only two forms of music allowed in their house are country and western.

"I've been contemplating it," she's mentions, "especially since I choreographed this routine to MC Dazzle's latest release. The song is called, If, and I absolutely like it. The beat is dope! Have you heard it, yet?"

Before I answer, she grabs her phone and plays the song,

"If I just keep on believing, nothing is impossible.

If I keep on moving forward, nothing is impossible.

What I believe in I will achieve in.

Nothing is impossible.

Nothing is impossible to him who believes."

"Told you. The beat is insane, and the lyrics are powerful, right?" Renee asks while dancing.

I must agree; the song is dope, and the words are inspiring! I could certainly visualize her performing her routine to the melody.

"That is the perfect song for you to do your dance," I say.

"You honestly think so?"

"I definitely do."

The park is so spectacular, and it is just what we need. It has been a long week, and with midterms coming up, the tempo is picking up quickly. Plus, Mom has been overseeing several severe cases, and she has been coming home more tired than usual. Dad invariably picks up the slack and steps in to keep the entire family calm, but the atmosphere in the house is shifting just a bit.

Coming through the front door, I notice Dad in the kitchen, making his famous pot pie. He is dicing veggies and asks if I would like to help. Wheeling over to the sink, I grab a pair of disposable gloves for my bionic hands; they are splash-proof but not waterproof. I wear gloves when cooking and helping in the kitchen.

When my folks brought me home from the hospital, Dad had his contractor modify the entire kitchen. He knew he and his baby girl would devote many hours together cooking, and he wanted nothing standing in my way. I can access the sink and all the appliances while sitting in my chair. The faucets and soap dispensers are touchless; all I have to do is wave over them. The entire house is practically touchless. In addition to being a great chef, Dad is also a techie. He installed systems that allow me to speak to nearly anything in the house. Lights, TV, radio, computer, phone. If he had his way, the doors and windows would be voice-activated, too.

I love cooking with my dad. He took cooking classes in high school, and later in college. He thinks he is world-famous and makes this

'Bam! Bam!' sound when he is done. It is his signature mark.

I recall as a kid, I would hear him shouting, "Bam! Bam!" and for a long time, I assumed he was calling me. When people would ask me my name, I would say, "Bam! Bam!" That is a running family joke.

As he meticulously dices carrots, onions, and celery, I help make the gravy. While stirring the oil and cornstarch, I add the seasonings. I am honestly becoming a good cook. I love that it doesn't matter that I use prosthetics. I'm at home in the kitchen, just like my dad.

He and Mom allowed me to wander and explore and to be creative. Before I turned eight and was fitted for my bionic arms, I learned to paint with my mouth and what remains of my arms. I dressed and even did my own hair. It was a challenge at first, but Dad jerry-rigged my hairbrush by developing an adjustable sleeve that I placed over my stump. I used it for my hairdryer as well. Now that I have my bionic arms, I can do hairstyles and put on my make-up; well, lip gloss and a little eyeliner. Dad says Jesus did a great job creating my face; I don't need to improve on perfection. I think this is just his way of keeping me his baby girl.

Both my folks have straight blonde hair; mine is reddish-brown and ridiculously curly. My womb-mom is White, and my biological dad, who no one knows for sure, must have been Black. So, I have thick dazzling hair and this magnificent sun-kissed skin. In the summer, I get such a deep brown tan, and I walk around like the Queen of Sheba. I absolutely love my looks. I am proud of them. I believe God knew I would be adopted by my parents because all three of us have the same deep dimples. People say we look alike, even with me being biracial. I do recognize a lot of me in them, and them in me. That can only be a God-thing, as Dad says.

He is telling me to add the chicken stock to the gravy because the veggies and meat are ready. I add it and stir gently. You must mix at just the right consistency, or the sauce will be lumpy, and no one in our household, not even the dog, will eat lumpy gravy. Once it's done, I go over and begin making the crust.

All our meals are made from scratch, Dad would not have it any other way. While lightly dusting the table with flour, I discuss my upcoming exam. We have a pretest session based on the questions I believe will be on the test. He, like me, was a straight-A student, and he is passionate about school. Yet one more daddy-daughter coincidence.

"With what are you having the most difficulty?"

"I'm not quite sure. I get the principles involved, and all, I just want to be sure I am wording the thoughts correctly for the essay portion of the test."

"We can go over it further after dinner if you'd like," he says as he places my perfectly formed crust into the baking pan. We then add the other ingredients, set it in the preheated oven, and go into the living room to chat. While we are talking, Mom walks into the room.

"What is that delicious smell?" she asks, "do I smell your famous pot pie?" She looks over at me, at the remnants of flour on my shirt, and smiles. "I appreciate that you two enjoy cooking together; you know that is so not my thing. I think God sent you here, Imani, so

Dad would have a cooking partner. Poor thing was near senseless just watching me sit at the table with my fork and knife in hand, salivating as I awaited food. I never actually got the hang of it, but your Grandma Mavis is a fantastic cook. I think she gives Dad a run for his money."

"The only running she gives me is to the bathroom after eating her food," he says, laughing so loudly his side begins to hurt. "You know I am only kidding. Don't go telling your mother I insinuated her food gives me diarrhea! You know how she gets about her cooking," he says as he peeks into the oven.

"She'd probably say the exact same thing about your cooking," Mom yells towards the kitchen.

"How was the park?" she asks as the two of us are waiting in the living room. "What juicy tidbits did Ms. CNN, I mean, Renee have for you?"

She knows Renee is the tell-all that is all to beat. She frequently reminds me of the phrase Grandma Mavis told her, "A dog that'll bring a bone will carry a bone." Meaning, be mindful of people who bring you gossip because they will more than likely talk about you to others.

"She is good," I say, "she has actually gotten much better about her gossiping since she started reading her Bible more. She wants me to enter a talent show that's coming up in a month. I think she should enter it with her dancing. She has been practicing a new form of hip-hop ballet, and she is fantastic! But, please don't tell her I described her being spectacular. Her head is already big enough. She will not be able to fit it through the door!"

"I won't mention a thing, mums the word. Why don't you want to enter it as well?" she inquires as Dad comes back into the room.

"Why doesn't she enter what?" he asks.

"Renee wants Imani to enter a talent contest, and Imani doesn't have a desire to do it," Mom explains.

As they are discussing it (as if I am not in the room with them), the timer buzzer dings. "Saved by the bell," I think to myself.

Mom and I head into the dining room as Dad retrieves dinner from the oven. After saying grace, we dig in. My dad is a fantastic cook, he absolutely is. Once we finish eating, Mom and I wash the dishes. While cleaning them, she tells me about the office building she will be moving into next month.

"By relocating, it will allow me to meet with the families in my office, and not have to travel as far. There is a play area for the younger kids; the play art therapists are in the same location. A larger facility enables us to assist more families," she explains.

I honestly cherish how passionate Mom is about her work. It is the reason why Janet believed she would be a perfect fit for me, and she was correct.

She continues to tell me all the details as we join Dad in the living room; he is tying his tennis shoes. Several nights a week, after dinner, we go for a relaxing stroll in our neighborhood. It is so picturesque, no matter the season. The trees, houses, and park are all spectacular. Other families in the area are out as well. Tonight, the weather is perfect. Dad and I discuss my test, and he has great suggestions for me. We pause and speak with a few neighbors as we walk, and before long, it is time to return home.

We say goodnight as we head to our rooms to read before preparing for bed. My folks have a rule: you must meditate on something positive before you go to sleep and as soon as you wake up. They believe in feeding our minds the same as we do our bodies. Dad says, "Imani, you have to feed your mind one book at a time." When I was a kid, I used to think he literally meant I was supposed to eat books. I cannot tell you how many books I chewed as a child. I came to like the taste of paper. Ha, just kidding. I truthfully did attempt to eat my books, though.

Chapter Three

Nightmare

Everything is pitch black. I'm on stage and am in front of thousands of people, I can make out words and sounds but not yet view faces. Suddenly the lights flood the darkness so brightly I am nearly blinded. The audience is chanting my name, "Imani, Imani, Imani." I glance down and observe a fantastic sound system with top-of-the-line equipment. The cheers begin to subside as I lower my headphones over my ears to spin a few tunes, then silence. I think the speakers have malfunctioned, so I click all the levers and knobs; still, nothing happens. I am horrified. People stand and begin booing and yelling for me to get off the stage! Someone begins to stomp their feet until everyone joins in. The noise is deafening. Suddenly a figure appears from behind the curtain. It zigzags across the stage, stands directly behind my chair, then proceeds to violently shove me off the stage! Not down the wheelchair ramp, literally OFF the platform! Panicking, I tumble forward, screaming, "STOP!" Thrashing about, I frantically make feeble attempts to grasp hold of anything to keep from falling. I cry out again, with a harsh raspy voice that sounds even foreign to me, "Please STOP!!!!!!!!"

"Imani? Sweetie, are you OK?" Mom says as she gently pats my shoulder.

Flailing by stumps in an attempt to attack whoever or whatever is after me, I realize I am no longer on stage. "What?" Struggling to comprehend where I am, I ask, "How in the world did you catch me? Did you witness who pushed me?" I am so disoriented.

"Honey, you were screaming in your sleep. What were you dreaming about?"

"I was dreaming?" I ask as my room comes into focus, and I now realize, Mom is sitting on the bed beside me.

"Yes, Honey. Is everything OK? Do you want to talk about it?"

"I dreamt I was falling off a stage," I tell her, not precisely divulging details about it. I don't know what the dream signifies if anything, so I don't want her to worry. Unlike my mellow Dad, Mom is a genuine worrywart!

She runs her hands through my curls as she sings. She may not be able to cook, but she has a fantastic voice. Dad says she easily could be a professional recording artist. I think he is right; she sings like an angel. As she sings a song, Grandma Mavis sang to her as a girl, I close my eyes and allow myself to get caught up in the sound of her sweet vocals. Somewhere in the process, I drift off to sleep.

Chapter Four

Cinnamon Rolls and OJ

"It's O-five hundred hours" blares my alarm. It is set on the 24-hour clock setting. Instead of saying "5 o'clock," it says, "0500 hours." It seems like I just recited my prayers before drifting off to sleep, so how can it be time to wake up already? I sit in bed a few extra minutes, then eventually get scooting, literally. I sidle over to my wheelchair. This one is smaller and lighter in weight; I use it in my bedroom and bathroom. It is also waterproof, so I use it in the shower.

Under the hot water, I allow my mind to go completely blank. I am obsessed with hot showers. It is my time for relaxation. While drying off, it dawns on me, I didn't read my morning devotional. Returning to my bed, I shuffle loose papers to uncover what I am looking for, my daily devotional book. Picking it up, I search and find today's date.

"When Jesus heard this, he was amazed. He said to those who were with him, 'I tell you the truth. This man has more faith than any other person I have found, even in Israel.'" Matthew 8:10. As I am meditating on the verse, a light tap sounds on my door.

"Imani, it's me, Mom. Is it OK for me to come in?"

"Yes, of course."

My door squeaks as Mom slowly enters, then gently closes the door behind her. Her brows are furrowed. I put my devotional down to give her my full attention.

"I just want to check in on you to be sure everything is OK. You know you can tell me anything, right? I mean, you and Dad are frequently talking, but I want you to know, I am here for you should you need to tell me anything. Absolutely, ANYTHING."

She says the last word like it has ten syllables.

"Mom, I know. But now you have me worried! Is there something YOU should be telling me?"

She lowers herself onto my bed, then gently places her hands on my chair. "Honey, your nightmare has me a bit concerned. I just want to be sure everything is OK with you, that there isn't anything occurring that I should know about, you know. I mean, is there something you need to share with me?"

"Oh, the dream. Everything is fine, Mom," I assure her. "I dreamt I was on stage about to DJ, and the equipment malfunctioned. People started booing, and then this guy, I think it was a guy, it was more like a dark figure comes from backstage and pushes me off the stage. Not down the ramp; he pushed me off the front of the stage. I must have been screaming so much in my dream, I did it in real life as well."

Upon learning it was just a nightmare was about music, she slowly exhales and gives me the tightest hug. After she lets me go, and I am breathing again, I must ask. "Mommy, what did you suspect?"

"Oh, you know me, such a worrywart. I just want to be sure nothing is happening that requires my attention. You know a mother's touch and all."

She talks a bit about the weather, then stands to leave. "I will let you get ready for your day. So glad we had time to chat. I adore you, Mani, more than life itself."

"I love you too, Mommy. Please know that if ever I need anything, I know I can come to you. You don't have to worry."

She smiles as she leaves my room. What I told you? Mom's a worrywart to the umpth degree.

I can't blame her for sometimes overreacting when it comes to me. Dad is the one who gives me enough space to build a country. Mom, on the other hand, is continuously hovering. She jokingly calls herself a helicopter mom. She witnesses firsthand so much negativity at work, I understand why at times she smothers me with affection.

I finish reading my devotional and get dressed. When I come out of my room, I smell homemade cinnamon rolls coming from the kitchen.

"I may not be able to perfectly roll dough, but I can squeeze oranges," Mom says as she places glasses of juice on the table.

"Wow, it smells delicious," I say, entering the kitchen.

"Nothing but the best for my ladies," says Dad, as he reaches into the oven and retrieves his homemade creations.

While eating, we discuss our day, and it never fails, Dad cracks his corny jokes.

"What do you call a pampered cow?"

When we don't answer, he says, "Spoiled milk!"

"David, that is not as funny as you think!" says Mom, as Dad doubles over laughing.

The bell rings as the door opens simultaneously. Renee waltzes in. She only rings to announce her presence. She's family and knows she's forever welcome.

"Hello Hicks family," she says as she takes a seat. "Mr. Hicks, is that the aroma of your famous cinnamon rolls my nose detects?" She asks the question while reaching across the table to grab one.

"No need to ask, Renee, you are always welcome to my creations," says Dad, passing her a napkin.

"Obviously thankful," she replies with a mouth filled with gooey rolls and icing.

Standing to leave, she reaches onto the plate to quickly snatch the remaining roll for the walk to the bus stop.

"I'd hate to leave this little guy on the tray all by himself; we'll call it one for the road."

While we wait for the bus to arrive, I tell Renee about my dream. She listens intently as I recall the details. I also tell her about Mom's reaction and her coming in to talk to me; she pauses before responding.

"What do you think the dream signifies?"

"I don't know. It could be because you have my head filled with all this nonsense about entering the talent show. Or because I've been obviously contemplating the meaning behind the Scripture verses from last Sunday. You remember? The story of Peter walking on water."

"Girl! Do you think it implies you can one day actually walk!" she whispers with eyes as wide as Dad's rolls.

"Renee, I don't … I mean, I don't think so. How could I walk? Look at my legs! You get what I mean? I don't know what it signifies. It could just be that I should not have had that third helping of my dad's pot pie."

"He knows he can cook. I would be eating all the time if I lived with you."

Just then, the bus pulls up. We wait for the back door to open; it has a ramp attached that allows me to enter the bus with my chair. Renee frequently rides up with me as she waves to her invisible subjects. She calls it her chariot.

Everyone is in rare form; the bus is extra loud this morning. Students are talking about, you guessed it, THE TALENT SHOW. Didn't I tell you it is a small town? Not a whole lot happening, so any news is enormous news.

"I most certainly will enter," says D'Wane. He plays the saxophone. He's probably not as outstanding as he thinks, but he is talented. He has been playing for a long time.

"I was talking to my instructor, and she thinks I should do my dance routine," says Marcia. Like Renee, she dances ballet, only it is traditional; she was in The Nutcracker. Not the lead role, but if you sit long enough, Marcia will tell you about every minuscule detail of the production. She'd have you believe she was not only the lead dancer but all the dancers, to include the soldiers!

"What if we form a singing group," says a kid with a huge afro. I can't recall his name. He is talking to a small group of boys, "We can be an all boy's band and sing some old school stuff. You know, the songs that make our moms scream when they come on the radio." Everyone starts laughing at that. I envision my mom, godmother, and grandma screaming over a Luther Vandross song. I can practically hear Janet yelling, "Now, honey chile' that's my song right there!"

I inquire if he is familiar with any Luther songs and he shrieks, "Come on now! Girl, you know I can sing Lutha!" and commences to belt out tunes at the top of his lungs. The girls on the bus impersonate groupies and are screaming their hearts out! Some are falling out of their seats pretending to faint! I must admit it; he has a magnificent voice.

Before long, the bus is hype! Everyone is belting out tunes from Country to Rock to R&B. The bus driver allows it for as long as she can take it, then silences the madness. "Pipe down back there. This isn't American Idol!" This makes the bus even louder with laughter. It is beginning to be a wacky day; I just sense it.

As Renee and I are making our way to class, I catch wind of someone whispering loudly, "How is she able to do her work with those fake arms? I have never seen anyone like that. Was she in a car accident or something? Oh, my goodness, where are her legs!"

Following the voice, I observe a girl I don't recognize. She catches me looking at her and jerks her head the other way. Renee picked up on her comments as well and is about to pounce. "I've got this," I gently say to my 'ride-or-die' friend, as I wheel over to introduce myself. I have found the best way to deal with misconceptions is to do so head-on.

"Hey," I say as I extend my arm in her direction, "my name is Imani. Are you new to our school?"

She isn't sure what she should do, so for a moment, she just stands there staring at her feet. When she discovers I am not upset or angry, she turns to look at me, then awkwardly shakes my hand.

"Yes," she finally says, "I'm new."

"Welcome. Where are you coming from?"

"Um," she answers, as she is looking at her hand in mine, "my family and I came from Texas; my mom is in the Army. We moved here last week."

"Oh, that's cool. My best friend's brother is also in the Army," I tell her as I let go of her hand and point towards Renee, who is still standing ready to pounce.

"What's your name?"

"I'm Jessica." She is now fixated on Renee, not knowing if she should run or stay.

"Well, Jessica, I'll answer your questions. No, I was not in an accident; I developed Meningitis B as a baby and had my limbs amputated. My bionic arms allow me to do almost as much as you can, except swim. I like my wheelchair, so I have decided not to get prosthetic legs. It's a pleasure to meet you. This is a great school, and I am sure you will enjoy it. We are one big, dysfunctional family. I look forward to getting to know you more. Have a great first day."

We say goodbye, and I wheel over to Renee.

"Wow, I would have totally handled that a lot differently," she says, stunned.

"I had to learn how to respond to people who have questions about my body. You can't be me and not know how to communicate with people. Not everyone has met someone who looks like me. Don't get me wrong, I would rather not have to deal with it. Not that I would want to be someone else, I appreciate being me, and I honestly love my life. I just would prefer to live in a world where people don't stop and stare at someone for being different. Heck, we are all different. Even identical twins have differences."

As we are talking the bell rings. Mrs. King is at the door and, eavesdropping on the entire exchange, smiles as we enter the classroom. "You continually make me proud of you, Imani," I reply thank you as we take our seats.

Chapter Five

Fearfully and Wonderfully Made

The morning goes by quickly. Before I know it, the bell rings for lunch. At our seats, we discuss the new girl, Jessica. Renee reiterates that she doesn't think she could handle people obviously staring or asking what she calls "stupidly dumb questions."

"Not everyone stares," I say. "Well, not directly, anyway. I don't mind people looking or even asking questions. I prefer they ask questions than to make assumptions. That drives me bananas. From the time I was a little kid, I knew I didn't walk like others or have hands, but I simply didn't understand how different I was until one day in 1st grade, a kid at the playground called me a freak. I couldn't understand why he was so mean.

Truthfully, at first, I didn't even know he was referring to me. I looked around, trying to figure out who he was talking about. Then it hit me! I was speechless for a few moments, not knowing what to do. Then I thought back to a verse I was taught in Children's Church, that we are all fearfully and wonderfully created in the image and likeness of God.

So, with as much bravery as I could muster, I asserted, 'It must be sad being you. My mom says, 'hurting people hurt people.' I love being me. I am fearfully and wonderfully made just as God intended. I have a mommy and daddy who adore me, and I have a great life. Maybe one day you will be happy on the inside like I am, and then you can treat people as people."

"Wow, you contemplated all of that. I think I just would have used what was left of my arm and whacked that jerk right upside his head!"

"You would not!" I laugh so loudly; others look our way. Renee instinctively knows what to say to lighten the mood.

"Yes, I would, believe me. I would have scooted right up and whacked the jerk just like this." She makes wild circular movements with her arms in the air. People walking by look as if she is having a fit. I die laughing.

"I would have been voted class president for it too, and would have had t-shirts printed up proclaiming, 'I whacked a jerk with my good arm!'" She is on a roll now. There is no stopping her.

Before she gets into her comedy routine, I explain my parents prepared me for situations like that. Since they couldn't be with me 24/7, they empowered me with positive words even as a little girl. I say, "I was raised with I Am... phrases. They were the first words I spoke."

"'Give me some ice cream!' were my first words."

Again, we are laughing so loudly, I snort, making us laugh even more.

"Listen, about this talent show thing," I change the subject, "have you decided if you are will enter it?"

"I have been wondering about it, especially with what I mentioned about my form of dance. The idea of Marcia entering has me a bit nervous. She is a GREAT ballet dancer. Did you know she was in…?"

"The Nutcracker? Yes, I know. Everyone knows."

"And with the way Luther sings…"

"Wait, is that his real name or are you just calling him that because he sings like Luther?"

"Nope, that is his real name. He says his mom enjoys Luther's music so much, she named him Luther. You'll never guess his middle name."

Before I can even answer, she says, "Van!"

"Then what's his last name?"

"Ross!"

"Oh, my goodness. Luther Van Ross! Well, at least he can back that name with good singing. Can you imagine if he was a horrible singer with a name like that?"

"Imani, I can't imagine having the name, let alone not being able to sing and have it."

As we continue discussing the talent show, I realize that deep inside, I am starting to envision being upon that stage, which is insane, especially after last night's dream. Maybe this is my way of stepping into the deep, deep waters. Before I can mention this to Renee, the bell rings, and it is time to return to our place of learning.

"Alright, class, I hope you all enjoyed your mid-day meal and are ready to apply all that nutrition to gaining knowledge. Clear your desks, we have a practice exam. This is a team project, and I want you to work as partners. If you know the answer, and it involves a process, I want to see the method you used on the paper. Show your work."

Renee and I do not partner in class; we do our group studying at home. In class, we are assigned to other students. My study partner is Carolyn; Karen is Renee's. I can make out Renee's giggles from the other corner in the room. She is such a clown!

"Hey, Imani, are you entering the talent show?" Carolyn asks as we take out the paper with the test on it.

"I don't honestly know. What about you? Are you considering participating in it?"

"Oh no, I don't have that kind of talent. Now, if it was an art or photography contest, that I would do. But nothing like singing, dancing, or reciting poetry. I understand you are terrific at DJing. I wish I could do that. I can't carry a tune, and you do not want to ever witness me on the dance floor!"

"I bet you are a good dancer. My dad says everyone can dance, some just not on beat." We both chuckle at that.

"I haven't decided yet," I tell her, and we begin to work on the test. I know Renee is over there trying to answer all the questions. She vehemently refuses to allow me to claim first place on this exam. She has come in 2nd place the last three tests, and she is vying to get that number one spot back.

Finally, the bell rings for the end of the day.

"Class, have a great weekend. I will see you all on Monday. Be sure to invest time reading, don't spend all your time playing video games. And get out and enjoy the fresh air! How about this, read outside in the fresh air."

We say goodbye and leave for the bus.

The conversation is a bit different, returning home than from earlier. Since it is Friday, kids are discussing the newest movie release, or what video game just launched. Renee and I plan whose house we will meet at this evening. Friday is our pizza and Netflix night. Dad repeatedly offers to make our pizza, but we like the sound of the doorbell ringing and the pizza guy coming to the house.

"Bring your pillow over," she says, "let's make it a sleepover."

Once the bus lets us out at our stop, I go home as Renee goes to her house.

Chapter Six

Walk By Faith

When I wheel inside, Dad is in the kitchen and looks up, "Hey, Mani, how was your day?"

"Overall, it was a great day. We have a new student who had questions about me. I used it as an opportunity to introduce myself to her and quash any misconceptions she may have," I say as I put my things away. "Her name is Jessica."

"One day, we will be in our new bodies and won't be tied down to these earthly vessels," he says. Told you he talks like a preacher. The only thing that my dad is more passionate about than his family and cooking is God. He has a way of talking about the Bible in a way that makes God appear so very real and close. He once told me that when he was a kid, his life was complicated. His parents fought all the time; dad spent a lot of time in his room, scared or crying. He never actually experienced having a loving relationship with his dad, so he found himself desiring to know more about God as his Father. He shared with me the first time he went to Children's Church, and the leader was preaching from John 3:16; he nearly ran over everyone to get to the altar. He felt by having Jesus in his heart, he would never be alone. He has walked with Jesus ever since.

"Dad?"

"Yes, Sweetie?"

"Did there ever come a time when you doubted the things you believe regarding God or began to doubt His realness?

"I am certain everyone experiences phases when our beliefs are tested. It's then that we can't walk by what we see, feel, or hear. I believe that is why the Scripture says we walk by faith and not by sight. If we can touch it, we don't need faith to receive it. For instance, if you want a bike, but already own one, then you don't have to use your faith, because you can already possess it. Now, what if you are trusting God for a bike, and not only do you not visualize one, you also don't have any money to obtain one. Well, in that case, you will have to use faith to believe God has heard your prayer."

"Like the missionaries we helped in Cambodia who use bikes as their main form of transportation?" I ask.

"Exactly."

"I believe in God, and I know He is real. I know He is with me every moment of the day. He has shown me that. Even when I was a baby in the hospital, all by myself, I now understand that I was never alone. He had people there for me, like Janet, who watched over me and who was there right when I needed her. God used her to bring me to you." Dad smiles as I say this and gives me a hug. "There are just times when I feel like I am having challenges with … everything and I don't know if it is OK to feel doubt or confusion. You know, am I permitted to NOT have all the answers?"

"Honey, it is more than normal to be clueless and to sometimes have doubt. What is not wise is to run away from God when those feelings come. When you feel like that, I want you to pause and ask yourself what it is that you are genuinely experiencing. Could it be that at the root of it you have fears, insecurities, or doubt? Maybe that is when you can say, like the man who went to Jesus and needed his son to be healed, 'Lord, I believe, but help my unbelief!'"

"It is possible even while believing to have unbelief?" I am shocked. I never realized I can have faith and STILL have doubt. I bet you probably didn't know that either.

"You wanna know something else?" he is asserting, "God isn't caught off guard by it. He creates a path for us to find our way to Him. He is our light in dark places."

"Thanks, Dad," I say as I give him a hug. Just then, Mom walks in the door with, you guessed it, her phone to her ear.

She waves as she goes to her room to put her things away. I also go to my room to get my pillow and a few things to take to Renee's. I have some items at her house and her at mine. We decided long ago to have a drawer at each other's homes just in case we got to having too much fun and wanted to have an impromptu sleepover. We have had a lot of those.

Mom and I come out of our rooms at the same time. She has already changed clothes, wearing her yoga pants and t-shirt. She is done with work and is ready to relax.

"Hey, Sweetie, how was your day?"

"It was a great day. How about you?"

"It was a bit challenging, but everything ended upbeat. We received a call regarding an infant boy that a few weeks ago was left at the doors of the fire station. They believe it may have been a young mother who dropped him off. He was just a few hours old when he was left there. He has been in the hospital since then. He received a clean bill of health, and so far, no one has come forward to say he is theirs," she tells me as we join Dad in the living room. "He is so adorable. As soon as I picked him up, he smiled. He actually reminds me of you, so tiny and so darn gorgeous. He is in one of our foster homes until, hopefully, we can find him an adoptive family."

As she talks, Dad goes to the kitchen and begins fetching items for their dinner. They usually have salads on Fridays because they will "go big" all weekend long, as he calls it.

"I will spend the night at Renee's tonight."

"Are you all eating food from a cardboard box?" he asks.

"Yes, we are."

"What a way to hurt your old man's feelings. You know I can whip up a pizza better than any Papa Hut ever can," he announces.

I know he can; his pizza is a thousand times better than anything that comes after a doorbell ring, but there is something fun about ordering out.

I give them a hug and go next door. Renee is outside waiting. It is a splendid night, so we sit on her porch and talk. The later it gets, the more fireflies and stars light up the darkness. After a while, her mom pops her head out and says the pizza will be here in just a few minutes. We decide to stay out until it arrives.

"Have you given any more thought regarding the talent show?" she asks.

"I have, and I am still not sure. I mean, I want to be in it, but I am not sure if I want to be up in front of people. I definitely think you should do it. Maybe you can show me your dance routine tonight. I will be a good audience. Without me competing, you might just have a chance to actually win."

Renee taps me on the shoulder just as the pizza guy pulls into her yard, flooding the darkness with his bright lights and upsetting the silence with his loud, head-banging music. By the time he makes it to the porch, we are giggling our heads off. Her dad comes out to pay for the pizza, and he carries it in for us.

That night, we watch Netflix, eat pizza in the den, and sleep on the sofa. It was a great sleepover.

Sunday, she decides to join me for church and sits next to me as Pastor Caleb preaches. The message is from 1 Peter 4:12. Don't worry, I don't waste time surfing the net, my phone is in my pocket because I brought my Bible to church. Renee and I both are turning pages as Pastor Caleb reads, "Dear friends, do not be surprised at the fiery ordeal that has come on you to test you, as though something strange were happening to you."

"Who can tell me what this Scripture passage indicates to them?" asks Ms. Lauren.

As I am looking down at the pages, Renee's hand goes up.

"Yes," Ms. Lauren says, as she points toward us.

"It suggests that we should not be surprised when difficult times come because we know that nothing can separate us from God's love, and we are in His hands, protected by Him."

"Absolutely," she says.

I look at Renee as if I am seeing her for the first time. I didn't realize she's been reading her Bible that much; I am so very proud of her. She looks back at me and smiles, then softly bumps her shoulder into mine as I whisper, "That was a great answer."

After service, we head over next door and sit in the reading nook. She tells me how she has been reading her Bible more since her brother left for Army Basic Training. Her mom gave him one to take with him, and since he has vowed to study his Bible, Renee felt she should be reading hers as well. I tell her how proud I am, and she smiles as I've never prayed witnessed before. She then tells me this morning she the prayer that's listed in her Bible. It is called the Sinner's Prayer.

"I didn't feel any lightning bolts or strong winds come through my room, but I did feel a peace I haven't felt in a long time, maybe ever."

"I am so excited for you, Renee. Literally, we are not only best friends, but we are also blood-relatives! We are now sisters in Christ."

As I am expressing this, Dad walks up to let us know their service is over, and it is time to go to lunch.

While eating, Renee and I tell Dad all about her answering Ms. Lauren's question in service and about her praying the prayer for salvation. Dad excitedly cheers and gives Renee a high five as others turn their heads to determine where the jubilation is coming from.

Chapter Seven

Operation Security

The next evening, Renee looks online for information about the talent show. She can't believe it; all but one slot has been taken. As she completes the application, she calls me. "Guess what?" She's yelling as soon as I answer. "You won't believe this! They only have one spot left for the talent show."

"Wow, seriously? Are you claiming it?"

"Duh, of course, I'm doing it now. That is unless you want it. I can give it to you if you want," Renee expresses.

Before I respond, she asks me the strangest question, "What if we do it as a duo? I can dance, and you can play the song. If I do my new routine, you can mix the beats. You have watched me do it enough to know the music and my moves; it is the perfect solution."

I can't even object because someone is ringing the doorbell. Wheeling over, I open it, and she struts in. "I completed the application on my phone while walking over," she announces with a grin. "We are teaming up to become an act!"

I stand there looking at her like she has grown three heads, my phone still to my ear.

"You can hang up now," she says. "Did you hear me? We are an act!"

"Oh, we will be an act, alright! Like Lucille and Ethel!" I chide as I place my phone down on the table.

Renee walks behind me as I wheel to the sunroom. We may as well begin to practice. I must admit; we do make a great team. We spend so much time competing AGAINST each other (in fun) but have never partnered up to do something together. I like the feel of it. We make a pact; we are not letting the others know about our collaboration. It's our little secret.

Each day after school, we quickly complete our homework, so we have plenty of time to practice. Our parents don't even know what is occurring in the den; they only know we are preparing for the talent show.

The evening of the event, Renee's family gets a surprise visit: it is Josh. He is home from Basic Training. Renee can't wait to tell him all about our routine. She begs him to please keep quiet until after the event. He gladly agrees.

When it is time to go, we grab our bags, all pile into their van and drive to the center. It's only a few miles from our neighborhood, but we leave early to be sure to get good seats. As we travel, both families are trying desperately to pry information out of us. Our lips are tightly sealed. Renee tells them to have patience, they will all discover soon enough. She winks at Josh, and he smiles back. Picking up on this, her mom tries to get Josh to spill the beans, "OPSEC," he responds.

"What exactly does that mean?" Mom asks.

"It stands for 'Operations Security,'" she says, "it is military speak for 'we have not been cleared to know.'"

"Oh," Mom laughs, "It's super top secret, is it?"

"With the way the girls have been behaving, I believe so."

"Then we will just have to wait and find out, won't we?" says Mom as she smiles at me.

Once we park and make our way inside, Renee and I quickly go backstage to change; our folks find seats near the front. It is a zoo backstage. Kids are all over the place, some looking so nervous I swear they are about to puke. I quickly maneuver my chair out of the way of one contestant looking for the trashcan. Just witnessing this is starting to make me a bit jittery. Flashbacks from my dream come flooding in, and I look for the exit doors.

Renee recognizes the look of panic on my face, runs over immediately, and gently whispers, "We've got this! Not only are we good, but we also have faith!"

Calming myself, I say, "If Peter walked on water..."

"Then you and I can definitely walk on stage!" says Renee with fantastic confidence.

"Well, technically, I will walk, and you will roll!" she says as she playfully shoves me. She has a way of getting me to focus on what is essential. Did I forget to say how much I like this crazy girl?

As the words are still coming out of her mouth, I hear our names called. Well, sort of, anyway. They announce us by our stage name. Yes, we have a stage name. Don't all famous artists? Over the audience applause, the MC repeats it, "And next to come to the stage is Faith Walker!"

Renee walks beside me as I wheel on stage. The audience goes silent and just stares. She's wearing her ballerina costume, I am dressed in all black leather, and my hair is in two afro puff ponytails. My wheelchair has halogen lights on the wheels. Even our families are speechless. I guess they were expecting someone named Faith. I turn to look behind me, believing this is the beginning of my dream coming true. I can just sense it; some ghostly figure is preparing to go from behind the curtain and shove my chair right off the stage. Suddenly, Josh stands and starts applauding and cheering at the top of his lungs. Everyone else joins in.

Chapter Eight

And The Winner Is...

I wheel over to the DJ booth, and Renee takes center stage. She absolutely radiates confidence. The crowd becomes silent with anticipation. Renee glances my way, smiles then nods for me to do my thing.

Unlike my dream, this time, when I pull down my headset, I hear the beat. More importantly, I feel it, deep down inside my soul. My eyes close and I sway back and forth, allowing the music to wash over me like gentle rain. When I open my eyes, Renee is leaping, twirling, and spinning! She looks like she is floating on air. We are doing it! We are doing it! I glance towards the audience and spot Mom, Dad, Grandma Mavis, Renee's folks, and Josh. They are spellbound and are clapping, stomping their feet. It feels so good!

I lift my headset as I stop the music to observe Renee rushing over to me, nearly knocking me out of my chair. She is screaming, "We did it! We did it!" As she pushes my chair to center stage, we both bow and bask in the applause. Backstage, our families rush in with flowers to greet us. It feels like a dream come true.

During our celebration, someone hears the announcer call Luther

Van Ross to the stage. As he commences to sing, the noise level drops to pure silence. The audience gasps at every note. He is genuinely a magnificent performer. We look at each other and say at the same time, "Oh, he hit it out the park. He won this thing!"

We all begin screaming his name as Renee falls to the floor, pretending to faint. We look like groupies. There's little doubt as to who the winner of the talent show is; I am OK with it. I am just so delighted to have been a part of the event.

"Can you believe we actually did it?" Renee is asking.

"Nope; had I not witnessed it myself, I never would have believed you two goofballs could pull it off," Josh says. We both give him love taps on his legs. It is good having him home, even if for only two weeks. Soon he will be leaving to go to AIT (Advanced Individual Training) in Ft. Polk, Louisiana. He will be there for a few more months, then receive his permanent duty assignment. While he is home, I know his family will be smothering him in attention, especially Renee.

She is excitedly rehearsing our performance moment by moment, and I join in. We are so engrossed we don't even hear the MC asking for Faith Walker to return to the stage. Dad yells out, "Hey, Shorty and CNN, they are calling your name!"

Renee prances beside me as we return to center stage, our families following close behind us, stopping near the curtain. We can hear them back there whispering loudly. Luther Van Ross and Marcia Scott are both already on stage. We cannot believe we made it to the top three! My mouth is wide open.

The MC has a glittery silver envelope in her hand, her assistant proudly standing beside her. Directly at her feet is the most gigantic trophy I have ever viewed in my life. It is nearly too tall to carry.

"Mr. Burton, would you kindly come to announce our winner," the MC says into the mic.

Mr. Burton appears on stage and receives the envelope. I feel like I am outside myself watching the Grammy Awards. Clearing his throat, he announces with his deep voice, "The winner of the 13th Annual Our Youth Our Future Foundation, Inc. Teen Talent Showcase is..." He then pauses for emphasis.

"What's with all this silence?" I hear myself whispering. Just then, Renee grabs me by the shoulder. I'm glad she does, as I may have stopped breathing, my chest is pounding with adrenalin. I look backstage and peep Dad silently cheering. He is genuinely such a character, and I appreciate him for it.

Turning my attention back to center stage, I hear Mr. Burton announces, "The winner is... Oh my goodness, I don't think we have ever had this happen before. Ladies and gentlemen, boys and girls, we have a tie for 1st place!"

The audience is cheering and stomping their feet. Renee stoops down and holds on to the armrest of my chair. I whisper to her, "No matter what, we are winners for joining together to form a team!" She looks up smiling, and we both take a deep breath.

"Our first 1st place winner of the 13th Annual Our Youth Our Future Foundation, Inc. Teen Talent Showcase is..."

"Get on with it," I hear my mom whisper (much too loudly) from backstage.

"Luther Van Ross!"

Everyone enthusiastically applauds so loudly we can hardly hear Mr. Burton speaking. Luther's mom rushes on stage, grabs him, dances around in circles, as she screams, "That's my son! I knew I gave you the right name when you were born!" She then snatches up the trophy as if it weighs only three pounds and struts off stage. The audience roars with laughter.

Finally, the hullabaloo subsides enough for Mr. Burton to be heard. He clears his throat again, for emphasis. As he does, Marcia walks over to us, and we hold hands in anticipation. "Ladies and gentlemen, boys and girls, I am proud to announce our second 1st place winner is...Faith Walker!"

Oh, my goodness! We actually won! Renee is doing cartwheels on the stage. I am so shocked I can barely move. Our entire family comes rushing onstage, and it is a chaotic scene. Josh is holding Renee in the air; her folks are jumping up and down. Dad wheels me around as Mom and Grandma cheer him on. Marcia comes to give us a congratulatory hug, and Luther comes back on stage to do the same.

After regaining the crowd's attention, Mr. Burton asks the audience to please give a round of applause for our 2nd place winner, Marcia Scott. Everyone cheers as she takes her bow and does a few spins! He passes her a ribbon and envelope. We all cheer as her grandmother comes on stage to stand beside her. There are photographers everywhere capturing pictures of us proudly holding our certificates, and Mrs. Ross with the trophy. She won't let anyone near it, not even Luther.

The 2nd place winner receives a $350 gift certificate; 1st place each receives $500. Luther quickly grabs the envelope with the money. Renee and I will split our winnings. The money is secondary, but I am still in shock! We won 1st place... well, we tied!

"I want to thank everyone for participating in this year's event. I anticipate having you all right here next year." He congratulates everyone who participated, as he smiles for the cameras. Once again, we all pile into the van to celebrate our winnings over ice cream.

Chapter Nine

New Addition

That night, I proudly place my certificate on my dresser for all to view, then say my prayers before settling in bed. I sense even before closing my eyes, my dreams will be vivid. My mind is wired from all the razzmatazz! One thing is for sure, I will not be dreaming of falling off the stage! This is one fear I can check off my list.

I am with Peter and the other disciples on a boat. The wind howls and the waves are violent. They toss the ship back and forth, and we are losing our fight with the storm. Waves crash against the boat as it takes on water, too much water. My chair is sliding from side to side. I am bracing as best I can. As if this isn't bad enough, someone screams out in fear, "Look, it's a spirit; we most assuredly will die!" Pandemonium breaks out. Wanting to witness for myself, I quickly wheel to the edge of the boat and peer into the darkness. Rubbing the saltwater from my eyes, I realize it isn't a spirit, ghost, or sea creature! It's the Lord!

"That's Jesus!" I yell as Peter rushes past me to find out for himself. Before he can utter a single word, I shout out loudly, "Jesus, if it is honestly you, declare it is OK for me to come and walk on water with you!"

Jesus responds by proclaiming, "Imani, I have been waiting for you to ask this question since the day you were born! Come, walk on water with me." I stand, and as I look down, I am walking with two unflawed legs; perfect in every way. I look at my arms, and they are not my robotic arms; they are flesh and bones just like my legs. I exit the boat, amid the waves and the wind, and I walk with Jesus. As we traverse towards the shore, we talk. I glance back to discover Peter and the other disciples rowing the boat behind us.

When I wake, I tell Mom and Dad about my dream. Dad has a million questions, but before I can answer, Mom says she has something to ask both of us. Dad and I look at her with anticipation.

As if searching for words, she finally asks, "Mani, what would be your response if I asked if you were ready to be a big sister?"

Dad looks at Mom and then at me like a cow looking at a new gate. I must have had his same expression because Mom begins to laugh at us both.

"Oh, my goodness, you two goofballs! No, I am not expecting, but I have been considering the baby boy we rescued last month, and I feel he is supposed to be a part of our family. I just want to have input from you both before I pursue it further. What do you think? I mean, is this something we can all take on as a family?"

After a moment of silence, Dad and I begin talking at the same time. The chatter started calmly then escalated into pandemonium. In our excitement, we shout over the other. "I have secretly desired to be a big sister and have a baby brother!" I exclaim.

"I have genuinely wanted to have a son! I mean, don't get me wrong, Imani, you will still be Daddy's baby girl, but I would love a son! Are you sure Maya, I mean absolutely certain?"

"When will we be able to meet my baby brother? How old is he? How much does he weigh? What color are his eyes? Does he have hair? When can we go shopping to buy the items for the nursery?" I am filled with questions and wonderment.

"I am so thankful you both feel the same way," Mom responds with tears in her eyes. "From the moment I laid eyes on that precious little baby, I heard God speak to my heart. At first, I had questions like, 'God are you sure?' Then I realized we are the perfect family for this handsome baby boy. I feel God even gave me the perfect name for him. While reading a baby magazine, I came upon the name Daijon."

"That's a delightful name, Mom, what does it mean?"

"Translated, it means 'God's gift of hope.'"

"Could his middle name be Walker?" I ask. "This will give him the same initials as Dad, DWH!" Overjoyed, Dad, pokes out his chest with pride, and beams.

"That is a perfect name, Daijon Walker Hicks! We have a lot to do before he can come to live with us, but I just know this is God's plan for our family."

The entire morning, we discuss the talent show, my dream, and baby Daijon.

Before long, I recognize that familiar ring at the door. It's Renee.

It is time for us to go to school. We have a test to take, and I am determined to claim my number-one spot. I am sure Renee has the same expectation. This time, there will absolutely be no ties.

Made in the USA
Middletown, DE
27 September 2020